The Perfect Rebel:

The Life and Death of Emily Davison

by

Deborah Chancellor

Illustrated by Julia Page

For Diana, who dared to wear a hat.

You do not need to read this page –
just get on with the book!

First published in 2010 in Great Britain by
Barrington Stoke Ltd
18 Walker St, Edinburgh, EH3 7LP

www.barringtonstoke.co.uk

ISBN: 978-1-84299-754-3

Printed in Great Britain by Bell & Bain Ltd

Contents

Chapter 1
Death at the Races

June 4th 1913

"Place your bets, please!" cried Tom.

Tom's father was a bookie and he had a betting stall at the Epsom Race Course. Tom helped his father out on busy days, like today. It was a special horse race event called Derby Day. The crowds were huge and everyone was out to have a good time. Men, women and children, rich and poor, were all dressed in their best clothes. The sun was out, and the air was filled with talking and laughter.

"Put a bet on the King's horse!" Tom called out to the passers-by.

As the people pushed past, a tall, slim woman bumped into the fifteen-year-old boy. She was wearing a long, thick coat, even though it was one of the hottest days of the year. She looked hot and bothered.

"Are you alright, Miss?" asked Tom.

The woman looked at him and a sad smile flicked across her face.

"Yes, thank you," she replied. "But I'll be even better soon."

Tom watched as she slipped away into the crowd. She seemed different from the many people who had come to the Epsom Race

Course to enjoy themselves. Tom sighed, and turned back to take some last minute bets.

It was almost 3 o'clock, and not long to go until the Royal Race. This was what everyone was waiting for – the King's favourite horse was running in this race. Excited crowds lined the course, waiting for the race to begin. Children waved flags and adults cheered.

"They're off!" a voice cried, to the sound of pounding hooves. The people pushed forward, straining to see the horses as they thundered past.

Tom watched from his father's betting stall. The King's horse was called Anmer. He was a long way behind in the race. Suddenly, someone in the crowd ducked under the barrier, and walked across the race course ... right in front of Anmer. Tom gasped. It was

that woman … she was waving something in her hand.

What came next seemed to happen very slowly. The King's horse reared up, throwing his jockey to the ground and kicking the woman in the air, like a rag doll. The horse lost his balance and tumbled, and the woman fell to earth with a sickening thud. Moments later the horse struggled up to complete the race.

The crowd watched in horror. A lady standing near Tom gave her husband a nudge.

"It's one of those women who want the vote!" she said. Sure enough, the injured woman was clutching the white, green and purple flag of the 'Votes for Women' movement.

"Those crazy women aren't fit to vote," her angry husband replied.

Tom squeezed his way through the crowd to get a better look. Policemen were forming a line to hold the people back. The royal jockey was carried off the course. The woman was covered in blood, and lay on the turf. Men were lifting her onto a stretcher.

"I know who she is!" Tom heard a policeman say. "It's Emily Davison. What a trouble maker! Her prison record's as long as my arm."

A doctor felt the woman's wrist to check her pulse.

"I don't think she'll bother you again," he replied. "We'll take her to hospital, but there's not much we can do for her there."

A few days later, Tom read a report of Emily Davison's death in his father's newspaper. He couldn't get her face out of his mind.

One question really haunted him.

Why had Emily Davison done what she did?

Chapter 2
Young Emily

1872–1895

The story began 41 years ago on 11th October 1872. A baby girl came kicking and screaming into the world. Her parents, Charles and Margaret Davison, called their new daughter Emily.

"She'll have to fight to get her voice heard in this house," Emily's mother used to say, as she rocked her restless baby to sleep.

Emily's father already had ten children, nine from his first marriage. Now he had another daughter.

Emily was lucky because her parents had enough money to feed a large family. When Emily was very small, the Davisons moved out of London. The first years of Emily's life were spent in the countryside, in a quiet village in Hertfordshire. Young Emily was bored stiff.

"Why can't I go to school, like my brother?" she asked her father. She had to put up with a dull tutor, while her older brother Alfred went away to school. It just wasn't fair.

"Alfred needs a good education to help him get on in life," Emily's father replied. Emily frowned. "It's not the same for you, my girl," he went on. "Everything you need to know, you can learn here at home."

Emily was a clever child. Tall and thin, she had golden hair, green eyes and a mocking smile. She knew what she wanted, and was stubborn enough to get it. Emily loved swimming, cycling and ice skating, much to her mother's despair.

"What's wrong with sewing and singing, Emily?" Margaret asked her daughter. "That's what other girls do."

Emily put her head to one side, pulling a face that showed exactly what she thought.

Above all, Emily adored reading. When she read a book, she dived into a world where anything could happen. *In the real world there are so many things I can't do*, she thought. *If only I was a boy, I could do what I liked*.

When Emily was ten, the family moved back to London. Emily was thrilled – would she go to school at last? Finally, Charles

Davison gave into his daughter's non-stop demands and sent her to High School, not far from the family home in Kensington.

"I'll make you proud of me, Father," Emily told him, her eyes shining with happiness.

Emily was a model pupil. Unlike her brother Alfred, she passed all her exams with flying colours. When Emily left school, her mother began looking for a man for her daughter to marry. But Emily had no such plans.

"I want to carry on studying, Mother," she said. "There's a new college in London that will take women – it's called Holloway."

"I thought that was a prison," her father said under his breath. He didn't approve – but as always, Emily got her way.

A year later, her parents moved north, to live in Northumberland near their family.

Emily stayed in London, buried in her books. Then disaster struck.

Emily's father died suddenly, leaving the family with money worries. Her mother had to open a corner shop to earn a living.

"I can't afford your college fees," she told Emily.

"Then I'll get a job and pay my own way," replied her daughter.

Nothing was going to stop Emily now. She sailed through her exams, and won a place at Oxford University. One summer, Emily was staying with her mother when she found out the results of her final exams.

"I got the highest mark!" she shouted, almost bursting with excitement. She snatched a jar of sweets from her mother's corner shop, and ran to the village green.

She found some children playing on the grass. "These are for you!" she cried, throwing the sweets up in the air for them to catch.

Emily had found success in a man's world – and she wanted everyone to know.

Chapter 3
Dark Days

1895–1906

Emily was ready to face the big wide world. She began looking for a job, feeling sure that her Oxford degree would get her what she wanted.

I'd really like to write for a newspaper, she thought to herself. *Then perhaps I'll get into politics one day.*

But Emily's hopes were soon dashed. There weren't many jobs she could apply for because she was a woman. The old bitter feelings came flooding back. It was like being a child again, staying behind while her brother went off to school.

"They won't even consider me for a job, because I'm a woman!" she complained to her mother. "To men, I'm just a second-class citizen!"

Her mother sighed deeply. Would Emily ever be happy? Sometimes she really worried about her daughter.

Emily had to earn money to live, so she became a governess. Teaching spoilt, rich children was not her idea of a brilliant career. For eight long years, Emily swallowed her pride and put up with it. But when she saw men doing all the things she wanted to do, she felt like screaming.

Then at the beginning of the new century, something happened to give Emily new hope. In 1903, a woman called Mrs Emmeline Pankhurst set up a group called 'The Women's Social and Political Union' (WSPU for short). Mrs Pankhurst argued that the law should be changed to allow women to vote. This was important, because it would give women a say in how the country was run, and what laws should be made. Mrs Pankhurst held meetings all over the country, and many women began to join her organisation.

Emily read about the WSPU group in the newspapers.

Mrs Pankhurst has a point, she thought. *If women were allowed to vote, things might improve for us. Perhaps we would get better jobs, for a start.*

Emily was now 31 years old, and working for a Mr and Mrs May and their two daughters in Kensington, London. Her employers didn't approve of the WSPU.

"Give women the vote?" spluttered Mr May over his toast one morning. He was reading about Mrs Pankhurst in *The Daily Mail*. "Everyone knows women have smaller brains than men. They can't be trusted to choose who rules the country!"

Mrs May nodded in agreement. She turned to Emily.

"Don't get any ideas from those silly suffragettes, Miss Davison," she said. 'Suffragettes' was the name the newspapers had given to women like Emily, who wanted the right to vote. Mrs May smiled at Emily.

"Just find yourself a good husband, and let him vote for you."

Emily bit her lip and said nothing. It was more than her job was worth.

They don't know what they are talking about, she thought angrily.

Time passed, and Emily did nothing. She was worried that she would lose her job if she joined Mrs Pankhurst's group, and she really needed the money. She didn't want to go back to live with her mother. But Emily felt like her life was going nowhere.

In November 1906, despite her worries, Emily went to a meeting of the WSPU. She agreed with everything the group stood for, and became a member straight away. Suddenly, Emily had found a use for her energy and brains.

"I'll never look back," she said, her heart pounding with excitement.

From that moment, her life changed forever.

Chapter 4
Flying the Flag

1906–1908

Emily began to lead a secret life. By day, she was a respectable governess, and by night, she worked for Mrs Pankhurst's group, the WSPU. She was careful to hide all evidence of what she was doing from Mr and Mrs May, her employers.

"I'm just going out for some fresh air," she would say as she left the family home in the evenings. Then she would make her way to a WSPU meeting, to discuss the group's latest tactics.

Emily's energy was noticed by the leader herself, Mrs Pankhurst. One evening, she called Emily to her office in the middle of London.

"I have an important job for you, Emily," she said. "I would like you to help organise an event in Hyde Park. It will be a chance to bring all our supporters together from around the country."

This was a very special request, and Emily knew it. She felt a rush of pride.

"I won't let you down, Mrs Pankhurst," she replied, smiling.

Emily spent every spare moment on her new task. Before long Mrs May began to ask questions. Did she know what Emily was up to?

"You look so tired, Miss Davison," she said to Emily one evening. "Why don't you stay in tonight?"

Emily looked down, avoiding eye contact.

"I like to make the most of my time off," she said, put on her hat, and hurried out.

On Sunday June 21st 1908, over half a million people came to Hyde Park to fly the suffragette flag, and the day was a great success.

"Well done, Emily," said Mrs Pankhurst soon afterwards. "You have worked so hard." But she looked serious.

"Is there something wrong?" asked Emily.

Mrs Pankhurst gave a frown.

"I'm afraid that the Prime Minister still won't let MPs pass a law to allow women to vote," she replied.

"Do you mean he's broken his promise?" cried Emily, stamping her foot in anger. She couldn't believe it. When the Liberal government had come to power two years before, they had promised to discuss women's rights.

"I'm sorry, my dear," said Mrs Pankhurst. Suddenly she looked older than her fifty years. "It seems that our peaceful protest hasn't changed a thing."

Emily was shocked, but a lifetime of disappointment had prepared her for this moment.

"We need to do something drastic to make the government sit up and notice," she said. She made up her mind to do something that she should have done long ago.

"I'm going to give up my job," she said firmly, "if you'll let me work for you instead."

Emily had a particular kind of work in mind. If she wasn't tied to a regular job, she could offer to do 'danger work'. This was the kind of work that the government couldn't ignore ... the kind of work that would get the WSPU group noticed, but could lead to a prison sentence.

"Are you sure?" asked Mrs Pankhurst.

"Very sure," Emily replied. "I'll make a perfect rebel."

So without looking back, Emily Davison took the first steps on her path to a criminal career.

Chapter 5
Rocking the Boat

1909

At long last, Emily felt a sense of freedom. The wages she earned from the WSPU group were just enough to live on, and she was doing something she believed in.

In March 1909, Emily had her first taste of direct action.

"Just wait until the Prime Minister sees our list!" she said to her suffragette friends as they marched to the Houses of Parliament. They were about to hand a list of supporters' names to the leader of the Liberal Party, Lord Asquith.

But the list never reached him. As the women got close to the government buildings, they were stopped by the police and arrested. Emily was sentenced to a month in Holloway Prison.

What would my father think of me now? thought Emily.

Life in prison did nothing to break Emily's spirit – if anything, it made her want to do even more for the group. A few months after she was released, Emily was arrested again. An important member of the government, Lloyd George, was giving a speech. Emily forced her way into the hall where he was speaking, to make a protest. She was not

surprised to find herself back behind bars in Holloway.

Emily knew several suffragettes who had refused to eat while they were in prison, and she admired what they had done. It wasn't long before she copied her friends' example.

"I'm going on hunger strike," she declared.

The prison guards couldn't decide what to do about this, but one thing was certain: Emily Davison was nothing but trouble. They were pleased to see her go when the prison governor let her out early.

Emily's time in prison changed her. The old Emily of the past, who had worried so much about losing her job, was gone forever. The new Emily was without fear and willing to do anything for women's rights. In September, Emily was caught red-handed, throwing fake bombs through the window of a political meeting.

"This is a warning to the government," she explained. "They should give women the rights they deserve."

Back in prison again, Emily complained that she was not being treated fairly.

"All I want is the vote, but I am not allowed to wear my own clothes and keep my things with me, like other prisoners accused of political crimes," she argued. In protest, she smashed seventeen windows, using a hammer that she had smuggled into the prison. Then she began another hunger strike. As before, she was released before her sentence was over.

"She'll be back quicker than you can say 'Mrs Pankhurst'!" joked a prison guard, as Emily walked free through the prison gates.

Only a few weeks later, Emily was arrested again, this time for throwing stones at Lloyd George. "The stones were wrapped in my favourite suffragette slogans," she explained. The police were not impressed.

Emily was sentenced to a month in prison at Strangeways, in Manchester. This time, the prison guards were ready for her. When Emily refused to eat, they held her down and forced a rubber tube down her nose and throat. Emily struggled to free herself, but it was hopeless. She almost choked as guards poured a thick soup down the tube. Emily had never been in such terrible pain, and she thought she was going to die.

Afterwards, when she was left to recover, Emily felt angry about the way she had been treated. She vowed to resist another time. When the guards came to force-feed her again, she piled furniture up against her cell door and blocked herself in.

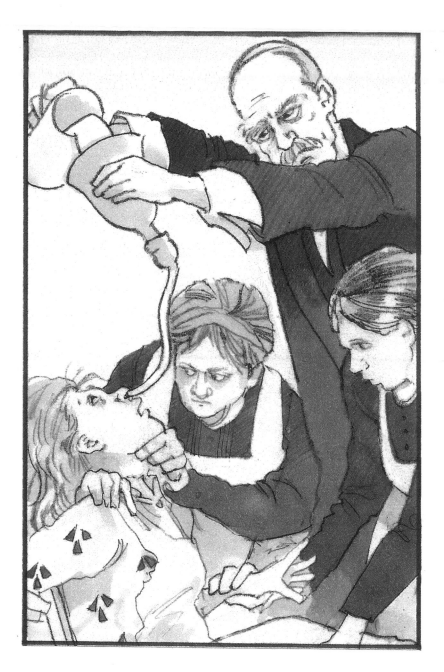

"Open up!" shouted a guard. There was no reply from Emily.

"We'll have to flush you out!"

Prison guards pushed a hose-pipe through Emily's window, and fired ice-cold water into her cell. Fifteen minutes dragged by. Emily stood her ground as the cell flooded.

"Break the door down!" ordered the chief guard. "If she drowns, we're in trouble."

The doors were forced open. Emily was shivering and soaked to the skin, but her spirits were soaring. She had forced them to stop. She was in control.

"Take her to the hospital wing," said the chief guard, shaking his head. "They can deal with her there."

When Emily left prison, she complained about her treatment.

"I'm going to sue those guards," she insisted. To everyone's surprise, she won her case, and was awarded £2 in damages. This was two weeks' wages.

Emily grabbed the head-lines in all the papers. It wasn't for the last time.

Chapter 6
Shock Tactics

1910–12

Emily was becoming well known – to the public as well as the police. Some of her friends thought this was a good thing.

"We need more fighters like you," said Mary Leigh, an active suffragette and one of Emily's closest friends. "Remember what we stand for. We have to take action, you know

– just sitting about and talking will get us nowhere."

Not everyone in the WSPU group agreed with this point of view. Some felt that Emily was in danger of pushing things too far.

"Be careful, Emily," warned Mrs Pankhurst. "We need to keep people on our side. If the people turn against us, the government will not change the law and give women the vote."

But Emily wasn't very good at listening to advice – she never had been. She would do anything to bring attention to the suffragette cause. On 2nd April 1911, Emily broke into the Houses of Parliament, where the government passed new laws. It was the night of the National Census, when everyone's names and addresses were recorded. Emily spent that night hiding in a broom cupboard, so she could claim her address was 'the Houses of Parliament'. The next morning she was discovered and dragged away by the police. "Women should be able to vote, just like men!" she shouted in protest.

This stunt was the last straw for the leaders of the WSPU group. Emily was too extreme – what would she do next? Emily knew when she wasn't wanted.

"I'm going to leave Mrs Pankhurst and her friends," she said to Mary Leigh. "It's time for me to act alone."

Leaving the WSPU group after five eventful years was hard, but once again, Emily felt a sense of freedom. *No one can tell me what to do now*, she thought. *I can do things my own way.*

The following year in December 1911, Emily set fire to some post boxes in Westminster, not far from the Houses of

Parliament. Emily had chosen her target well. Post was the main way people got in touch with each other, so many people were affected. Important letters and documents were destroyed without any warning. News about what Emily had done spread fast. This was just what Emily wanted.

Emily's crime was serious, and she had to pay the price. At her trial at London's Old Bailey, she was sentenced to six months in prison. This would be her longest spell yet behind bars.

It's back to Holloway again, she thought grimly. *My second home.*

The long months in prison seemed to stretch on forever. As time passed, Emily became ill from the hunger strikes, and the terrible force-feeding that always followed them. One day in June 1912, she was feeling desperate.

I can't go on any more, she thought. *I must make a stand against this cruelty.*

When a prison guard was looking the other way, Emily threw herself off a high staircase. Her fall was broken by some wire netting, but she hurt her back very badly.

"Why did you do it?" the prison governor asked Emily, as she recovered in the hospital wing. "You could have died."

Emily looked away and sighed. She had hoped that her death would stop other people having to suffer.

"I thought one big tragedy would save others," she replied sadly.

Chapter 7
Mistaken Identity

November 1912

Emily was feeling depressed. When she left Holloway Prison later that summer, she couldn't stop thinking about what had happened.

"Perhaps it would have been better if I had died in there," she said to her friend Mary Leigh. Mary was shocked.

"How could you say such a thing?" she replied. "We still need you to fight for women's rights!"

But Emily wasn't listening.

"Prison wouldn't be the right place to die," Emily muttered. "The government would probably cover it up, and no one would ever get to hear about it."

The government was in fact very worried that such a thing might happen – Emily was not the only suffragette who had almost died in prison.

In Parliament, MPs started to discuss making a new law, which would let prisons release suffragettes when they went on hunger strike. They would arrest the women again when they were strong enough to finish their prison sentence. This law was called the 'Cat and Mouse Act', because of the way a cat plays with its prey before it kills it.

Emily felt betrayed by the government. They said they supported the idea of votes for women, but all they ever did was make life harder for the suffragettes.

"They have let us down with all their lies and broken promises," she complained to Mary. "That man Lloyd George is the worst of the lot. He says he wants to help us, but he refuses to vote for a change in the law."

Mary agreed with Emily, but she was worried about her friend. Sometimes, it seemed that all the hunger strikes and force-feeding had done something to Emily's mind. Women's rights were all she thought about. Lloyd George had become her new pet hate.

"I don't know what I'd do if I ever met that man," Emily confessed to Mary.

Then in November 1912, Emily's moment came. She was travelling in Scotland and was at Aberdeen station, waiting for a train back to London. The platform was crowded with travellers, and there was plenty of bustle and noise. Suddenly, Emily saw a familiar figure walking ahead of her – it was Lloyd George! Shaking with anger, Emily went up to the man, and began to attack him. She hit him again and again with a riding stick.

As passengers and station porters pulled Emily back, she realised what she had done – it wasn't Lloyd George after all.

"Excuse me, madam," cried the man, struggling to his feet. A cut on his cheek was bleeding, and he was in a state of shock and confusion.

"I'm a minister of the Baptist Church," he said. "Who, if I may ask, are you?"

It was not Emily's finest hour. She was arrested, and sent to prison for ten days. As before, she went on hunger strike, and was let out soon afterwards.

Emily didn't know it, but she would never set foot inside a prison again.

Chapter 8
Bomb Plot

February 1913

It was a cold, miserable Christmas. Emily went to visit her mother at her village home above the corner shop. Before long, the two of them began to argue.

"Take a long, hard look at yourself, Emily," said her mother one day. "You're all skin and bones. This fight for women's votes is killing you."

Emily looked at her mother with her old stubbornness, shaking her head.

"We've got to make everyone see how angry we are," she replied. "We have to make ourselves heard."

"Well, you've certainly got my neighbours talking," sighed her mother. "They know exactly what you're up to, and they're not impressed. They can't understand how a good girl from a nice family like you can do such shocking things. And I must say, neither can I."

"Mother, why won't you listen?" asked Emily. "This is a war."

"Yes, but will you survive the fight?" asked her mother, with tears welling up in her eyes.

Emily went back to London in the New Year, and her attention soon turned to her old enemy, Lloyd George. She began plotting with a small group of extreme suffragettes.

"Have you heard that Lloyd George is having a house built?" she told her friends. "It's in Walton Heath, in Surrey. I've got an idea ..."

Over the next few weeks, the group planned a bomb attack on Lloyd George's new house. This time, the bomb Emily used was real, not fake. At 6am on 18th February 1913, an explosion tore through Lloyd George's house, destroying five rooms. The suffragettes knew the house would be empty at this time, and no one was hurt.

The next morning, the newspapers were full of the story. This was one of many crimes they could blame the suffragettes for. Since the beginning of the year, fires had been started in stately homes and stations, and telephone wires had been cut. Suffragette slogans had even been burnt onto golf courses.

Emily and her group of helpers were delighted to see that they had hit the headlines. They had covered their tracks well, and were confident they would not be caught.

"This was an important battle!" Emily declared to her friends.

But Emily's good mood didn't last long. The police wanted to punish someone for the bomb attack – they needed someone to blame, to show they were doing something. The day after the bomb attack, Mrs Pankhurst stepped forward.

"I'm responsible for this crime and for others like it," she said. "I did not take this action myself, but I admit that I inspired other people to break the law."

That was the excuse the police – and the government – needed to arrest Mrs Pankhurst. She was put on trial and sentenced to three years in prison.

Emily was horrified. She still looked up to Mrs Pankhurst, despite their differences. Three years in Holloway Prison was such a long time ... Emily thought about her own prison experiences, and a shudder ran up her spine.

Mrs Pankhurst is innocent! she thought. *Why should I go free, while she is behind bars?*

Emily asked herself this question over and over again.

Chapter 9
Final Act

February – June 1913

Angry and upset, Emily went home to her mother. She needed to rest, and to think about her future.

"I see they've arrested your leader," said Emily's mother as she greeted her at the door. "Perhaps things will calm down now for a while."

Emily couldn't face another argument, so she didn't reply. A sharp pain shot up her back – she was still recovering from injuries caused by her fall in prison. Her face went white, and her mother frowned.

"You're not well, Emily," she said. "You used to be so fit and strong, but now look at you! Forty years old, and you're like an old woman. Promise me you'll never go on hunger strike again."

Emily gave a shrug. In the last four years she had been force-fed in prison 49 times. Would she make it to 50?

That spring, Emily stayed with her mother, who lived near some stables. Emily spent hours watching horses trot down the lane behind the house. An idea formed in Emily's mind. As the horses passed by, Emily started to practice throwing large flags over their backs.

Emily had a plan. A famous horse race was taking place in a few months' time. Emily needed to practice what she was doing, to be ready for the big day.

The King's horse will be there, she said to herself. *If I get this right, I can throw the suffragette flag over the horse just before he crosses the finishing line. That will make a great photograph for the newspapers.*

The weeks flew by, and soon it was time to return to London.

On the morning of Wednesday June 13th, Emily went to Victoria Station and bought a return ticket to Epsom. It was a hot day, and she wished she could take off her coat.

It's a pity I've got to hide my flag up my sleeve, she thought. *But I can't let anyone see it just yet.*

Sitting on the train for Epsom, Emily checked her pocket book. She had meetings planned for the next week. Suddenly she felt cold, despite the summer heat. What if it all went wrong? She was taking a terrible risk. She had to face the possibility that things might not go to plan.

I should have written to my mother, she fretted. *I haven't told anyone what I'm planning to do.*

Looking out of the window at the clouds high in the sky, she pushed these dark thoughts to the back of her mind.

Three hours later, Emily walked onto the race course at Epsom, right into the path of the horses. As she reached for the reins of the King's horse, she pulled out her suffragette flag. The last thing she saw were the white, green and purple colours floating in the air. Then it all went black.

Emily's mother refused to travel down to London to visit her daughter as she lay dying in hospital. She was angry at what Emily had done, and stunned with grief. There was a knock at her door – it was a newspaper reporter.

"Are you proud of your daughter?" asked the smart young man.

Mrs Davison sighed. She remembered that when Emily was young, she had wanted to write for a newspaper. It seemed such a long time ago.

"I just want her back," she said, and closed the door.

Chapter 10
After the Funeral

1913–1918

Tom, the bookie's son, made up his mind to go to Emily Davison's funeral. Ever since he had met Emily at the Epsom Derby, he had thought a lot about what the suffragettes stood for.

"You should come too," he told his mother and younger sister, Lettie. "You're old enough, Lettie, you'll be thirteen in a few weeks' time. Emily Davison was trying to help girls like you."

"I haven't got time to waste," said his mother. "That woman was mad and dangerous. Women would have the vote by now, if it hadn't been for people like her."

Tom's father came into the room.

"Emily Davison's got everyone talking, hasn't she?" he said. "You can say what you like about those suffragettes, but they know what they want. They'll get the vote one day, I'd lay a bet on it."

Tom looked at his sister.

"Are you coming then, Lettie?" he asked.

"I think Emily Davison meant well," she replied in a low voice, looking at her mother.

"I'll come with you, Tom," his sister said.

A few days later, Tom and Lettie joined the huge crowds of people who gathered in London for Emily's funeral. There was silence as Emily's coffin passed by on its way through the city streets. Tom and Lettie stared at the rows of suffragettes who were marching behind the coffin. They were all dressed in white. Emily's coffin was covered in a cloth decorated with a large arrow.

"What's that?" asked Lettie in a whisper.

"It's the kind of arrow you get on prison clothes," Tom answered. "Emily did a lot of time in prison."

"I hope it was worth it," replied Lettie. "I hope it wasn't all for nothing."

Tom and Lettie followed the crowds and ended up at a big train station called Kings Cross.

"What's happening now?" asked Lettie.

"I think the coffin is being taken away on a train," replied Tom. "They're going to bury Emily at her family's church, somewhere up north."

"She's going home, then," said Lettie.

"I suppose so," said Tom. "Let's go home too."

A year later, Tom and Lettie's lives changed forever. In August 1914, the First World War broke out. Tom was sixteen, and lied about his age so he could go to fight in France. Many boys of Tom's age became soldiers. During the war hundreds of thousands of British soldiers were killed.

The girls who were left behind did jobs that were usually done by men. When Lettie was fifteen, she went to work in a factory, and earned a good wage. Women like Lettie worked hard and proved that they deserved to vote. No one could argue against the idea any more.

Tom was lucky, and lived through the war. When he returned home four years later in 1918, the law had changed. Women over thirty years old were now allowed to vote.

When he heard this news, Tom gave his sister Lettie a hug.

"Not long before you can choose the next Prime Minister!" he said. "Emily Davison would be so proud of you!"

He had never forgotten the suffragette's sad face at Epsom, all those years ago.

"If Emily were alive today, she'd be laughing," Lettie replied.

"She got her way in the end."

AUTHOR CHECK LIST

Deborah Chancellor

What made you want to write this book?

Emily Davison, because she was an amazing woman who did everything she could to help give women more rights. Today, Emily's story is almost forgotten ... but not quite. I wanted to write it down so more people could hear about it.

Who is your role model?

My daughter Imogen is my role model. She never lets her dyslexia stop her from trying her best, and being really cheerful about everything that she does.

Which suffragette do you most admire?

The suffragette leader Emmeline Pankhurst. She stood up for her beliefs, even though it didn't make her popular with some people. She really wanted to make a difference to the world she lived in.

If you could meet Emily Davison, what would you say to her?

I would ask Emily what I should say to people who can't be bothered to vote.

ILLUSTRATOR CHECK LIST

Julia Page

Who is your role model?

I have lots of role models. Quentin Blake, the illustrator, and Jenny Saville, the painter, have been role models for me. They have always kept true to themselves. Their work, each in its own way, is like no one else's, and is full of energy.

If you could meet Emily Davison, what would you say to her?

Thanks!

If you had the chance to time travel, which moment in time would you visit?

The 1930s. The reason I would choose to travel back to this time is because I love the clothes people wore in those days!

What do you think is worth fighting for?

The underdog.

What is the worst job you ever had?

Sticking soles onto the bottom of shoes in a factory.

Barrington Stoke would like to thank all its readers for commenting on the manuscript before publication and in particular:

Jade Ackers
Kathy Baugh
Hannah Boswell
Daren Carney
B. A. Christopher
Tyler Dedman
Chanelle Faseia
Raymond Gerrard
Elly Gray
Leeanna Husan
Jake Mason

Ben Murphy
Stephanie Nimmo
Brandon Ormond
Dale Osborne
Andy Pitchford
Andrew Place
S. A. Proudlove
Rita Smith
Ryan Stewart
Julie Sutherland
Jack Wooding

Become a Consultant!

Would you like to be a consultant? Ask your parent, carer or teacher to contact us at the email address below – we'd love to hear from them! They can also find out more by visiting our website.

schools@barringtonstoke.co.uk
www.barringtonstoke.co.uk